I CAN S

sight words

High Frequency Words

What are
High Frequency Words?

High Frequency Words, also known as 'sight words', are essential words that children need to learn in order to tackle reading simple texts.

They are common words that often have irregular or difficult spellings. They need to be practised and memorised by sight, so that children do not need to decode them or sound them out.

These High Frequency Words are based on Dolch's list of basic sight words and Fry's list of most essential words.

This spelling book is designed to be used either on its own or may be used to complement the popular Wordshark™ computer program to reinforce reading and spelling.

sight wrds

Instructions

This booklet is designed to encourage parents and teachers to work together by:

1. Parents using the workbook at home to help their children learn and memorise sight words; and

2. Teachers using the workbook in the classroom to monitor, assess and record children's individual progress

How to Learn the Spellings

*   read the spelling aloud, then ask the child to repeat the word
*   in the 1st column, trace over the spelling using a pencil (not a pen)
*   in the 2nd column, copy the spelling and say the word aloud at the same time
*   in the 3rd column, cover up the word and spell it from memory
*   in the 4th column, spell the word again from memory with eyes closed (It doesn't matter if the spelling goes outside the box or the writing is wobbly - this is the fun bit!)

Learning through Fun

If you find a word particularly difficult to remember, you can use a variety of fun, kinaesthetic learning methods such as writing the word in sand, in the air, with paint, using bright coloured pipe cleaners or constructing a word in 3D using modelling clay.

You can design card games using flash cards and colourful pens. Write the spelling on the front of the flash card, and on the reverse, write a mnemonic you have made up and draw a memory-jogger picture.

You can also use visualisation techniques. Take a pretend camera shot of the spelling, close your eyes, visualise the spelling and recall how many vowels there are, the colours, sizes and shapes of the letters. Then open your eyes and look up to the left to recall what you can 'see'. Spell out the word forwards, then try and spell it backwards.

The ultimate test is if you can then spell the word backwards, then you can spell it forwards!

Good luck in learning your spellings!

Example of a mnemonic

laugh

front of flash card

laugh <u>a</u>nd <u>u</u> <u>g</u>et <u>h</u>appy

reverse of flash card

3

Monitoring and Assessing Progress

The testing section at the back of the booklet is for teachers or parents to record spelling test results. If a word is spelled correctly, write a ✓ (tick) in the column; if a word is spelled incorrectly, write a • (dot).

Three consecutive ticks are required before the spelling is considered learned and committed to memory. If the child achieves a ✓ then a •, the child must carry on until he/she achieves three consecutive ticks: ✓ • ✓ ✓ ✓

Once spellings have been learned, they need to be practised regularly in order to be transferred from short-term to long-term memory.

For more ideas and information go to **www.icanspell.co.uk**

Date _____

Read then trace over	Copy and say aloud	Cover and spell	Close eyes and spell
up			
and			
on			
at			
is			
am			

How am I doing? ☺

Parent checked _____ Teacher checked _____

5

Date

Read then trace over	Copy and say aloud	Cover and spell	Close eyes and spell
cat			
cat			
dog			
big			
mum			
dad			
get			

How am I doing?

Parent checked

Teacher checked

6

Date _____

Read then trace over	Copy and say aloud	Cover and spell	Close eyes and spell
cat		cat	
in			
it			
yes			
can			
a			

How am I doing? ☺

Parent checked _____   Teacher checked _____

7

Read then trace over	Copy and say aloud	Cover and spell	Close eyes and spell
I			
we			
me			
he			
she			
go			
no			
so			
my			

How am I doing?

Date

Read then trace over	Copy and say aloud	Cover and spell	Close eyes and spell
this			
look			
like			
for			
said			
you			
are			

How am I doing?

Parent checked _____   Teacher checked _____

Read then trace over	Copy and say aloud	Cover and spell	Close eyes and spell
going			
they			
away			
play			
to			
come			
said			

How am I doing?

Parent checked _____   Teacher checked _____

Date _____

Read then trace over	Copy and say aloud	Cover and spell	Close eyes and spell
cat		cat	
went			
day			
the			
all			
was			
see			
of			

How am I doing?

Parent checked _____   Teacher checked _____

Read then trace over	Copy and say aloud	Cover and spell	Close eyes and spell
cat		cat	
an			
as			
back			
bed			
but			
did			
dig			
from			

How am I doing?

Parent checked _____

Teacher checked _____

Date

Read then trace over	Copy and say aloud	Cover and spell	Close eyes and spell
got			
had			
has			
him			
his			
if			
jump			
just			

How am I doing? ☺

Parent checked   Teacher checked

Read then trace over	Copy and say aloud	Cover and spell	Close eyes and spell
cat		cat	
man			
much			
must			
next			
not			
off			
ran			

How am I doing? ☺

Parent checked _____   Teacher checked _____

Date _____

Read then trace over	Copy and say aloud	Cover and spell	Close eyes and spell
than			
that			
them			
then			
us			
will			
with			

How am I doing?

Parent checked _____   Teacher checked _____

Read then trace over	Copy and say aloud	Cover and spell	Close eyes and spell
cat		cat	
came			
made			
make			
name			
home			
take			
time			

How am I doing? :-)

Date

Read then trace over	Copy and say aloud	Cover and spell	Close eyes and spell
ball			
call			
called			
push			
pull			
put			
live			
lived			
love			
have			

How am I doing?

Parent checked _____   Teacher checked _____

Read then trace over	Copy and say aloud	Cover and spell	Close eyes and spell
after			
again			
another			
be			
been			
because			
boy			
brother			
by			

How am I doing?

Parent checked _____   Teacher checked _____

Date _____

Read then trace over	Copy and say aloud	Cover and spell	Close eyes and spell
door			
down			
good			
took			
help			
her			
here			
house			
how			
now			

How am I doing?

Parent checked _____   Teacher checked _____

19

Read then trace over	Copy and say aloud	Cover and spell	Close eyes and spell
may			
more			
over			
our			
out			
about			
once			
one			

How am I doing? ☺

Parent checked _____ Teacher checked _____

Date

Read then trace over	Copy and say aloud	Cover and spell	Close eyes and spell
there			
these			
three			
what			
when			
where			
who			

How am I doing?

Parent checked _____   Teacher checked _____

Read then trace over	Copy and say aloud	Cover and spell	Close eyes and spell
cat		cat	
saw			
some			
seen			
tree			
very			
way			
were			

How am I doing?

Date

Read then trace over	Copy and say aloud	Cover and spell	Close eyes and spell
first			
do			
don't			
girl			
half			
laugh			
new			
night			

How am I doing?

Parent checked _____ Teacher checked _____

Read then trace over	Copy and say aloud	Cover and spell	Close eyes and spell
cat		cat	
water			
old			
many			
last			
school			
could			
would			
should			

How am I doing? ☺

Parent checked _____   Teacher checked _____

set		Date _____	
Read then trace over	**Copy and say aloud**	**Cover and spell**	**Close eyes and spell**

How am I doing?

Parent checked _____   Teacher checked _____

set |

Read then trace over	Copy and say aloud	Cover and spell	Close eyes and spell

How am I doing? 😊

Parent checked _____   Teacher checked _____

Use this section of the book to assess and record individual progress

Log spelling results in the columns as shown in the example below. If the child achieves a ✓ then a •, the child needs to relearn the incorrect spelling until three consecutive ticks are achieved: ✓• ✓✓✓

set		11th May	14th May	16th May	17th May	19th May
Date tested						
	cat	✓	•	✓	✓	✓

I CAN SPELL – Ready, Steady, Go... 😳

✓✓✓ = I can spell   • = I need to practise

1.1	Date tested									
	up									
	and									
	on									
	at									
	is									
	am									

set

1.2	Date tested									
	cat									
	dog									
	big									
	mum									
	dad									
	get									

I CAN SPELL – Ready, Steady, Go... 😊

set	✓✓✓ = I can spell • = I need to practise

1.3	Date tested									
in										
it										
yes										
can										
a										

set										

1.4	Date tested									
I										
we										
me										
he										
she										
go										
no										
so										
my										

I CAN SPELL – Ready, Steady, Go...☺

set		✓✓✓ = I can spell • = I need to practise										
1.5	Date tested											
	this											
	look											
	like											
	for											
	said											
	you											
	are											

set												
1.6	Date tested											
	going											
	they											
	away											
	play											
	to											
	come											
	said											

I CAN SPELL – Ready, Steady, Go... 😊

✓✓✓ = I can spell   • = I need to practise

set 1.7	Date tested									
	went									
	day									
	the									
	all									
	was									
	see									
	of									

set 1.8	Date tested									
	an									
	as									
	back									
	bed									
	but									
	did									
	dig									
	from									

I CAN SPELL – Ready, Steady, Go...☺

✓✓✓ = I can spell • = I need to practise

set

1.9	Date tested										
got											
had											
has											
him											
his											
if											
jump											
just											

set

1.10	Date tested										
man											
much											
must											
next											
not											
off											
ran											

I CAN SPELL – Ready, Steady, Go... 😊

✓✓✓ = I can spell   • = I need to practise

1.11	Date tested									
	than									
	that									
	them									
	then									
	us									
	will									
	with									

1.12	Date tested									
	came									
	made									
	make									
	name									
	home									
	take									
	time									

33

I CAN SPELL – Ready, Steady, Go... 😊

set		✓✓✓ = I can spell • = I need to practise									
1.13	Date tested										
	ball										
	call										
	called										
	push										
	pull										
	put										
	live										
	lived										
	love										
	have										

set											
1.14	Date tested										
	after										
	again										
	another										
	be										
	been										
	because										
	boy										
	brother										
	by										

I CAN SPELL – Ready, Steady, Go... 😊

set

1.15 Date tested									
door									
down									
good									
took									
help									
her									
here									
house									
how									
now									

set

1.16 Date tested									
may									
more									
over									
our									
out									
about									
once									
one									

I CAN SPELL – Ready, Steady, Go... 😊

✓✓✓ = I can spell   • = I need to practise

1.17	Date tested										
	there										
	these										
	three										
	what										
	when										
	where										
	who										

set

1.18	Date tested										
	saw										
	some										
	seen										
	tree										
	very										
	way										
	were										

I CAN SPELL – Ready, Steady, Go... 😊

set

1.19	Date tested									
	first									
	do									
	don't									
	girl									
	half									
	laugh									
	new									
	night									

set

1.20	Date tested									
	water									
	old									
	many									
	last									
	school									
	could									
	would									
	should									

I CAN SPELL – Ready, Steady, Go... 😊

set		✓✓✓ = I can spell • = I need to practise								
	Date tested									

set										
	Date tested									

Spelling Achievement Award

sight words

Congratulations to

For excellent spelling of
150+ High Frequency Words

Date _____

Signed _____